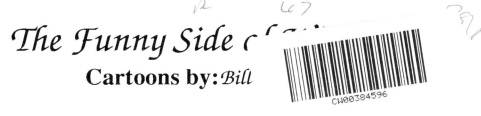

The Funny Side of...

Cartoons by: *Bill*

FOR MY DAD
PC 969 RONALD STOTT
LANCASHIRE CONSTABULARY

and

Thanks to Ian Boumphrey for thinking up most
of the jokes and supplying most of the wine

Origination by: Ian Boumphrey - Desk Top Publisher
Published by: Ian & Marilyn Boumphrey
                    "The Nook" Acrefield Road
                    Prenton Wirral L42 8LD

Printed by: Eaton Press Ltd
                    Westfield Road Wallasey Merseyside L44 7JB
ISBN   0-9507255-6-0

Price
£2.99

"Look Mam! Ayr oil!"

"New Brighton Tower, son - was one of the largest structures in Europe a bit like your Auntie Doris......"

"Yes - we have a massive sailing fraternity on Wirral - and there goes a substantial part of it!"

"Ooh! I wonder if we could get _YOU_ some of that?"

"I don't hold with all this new First Division posing - there's nowhere near as much to grumble about as when they were in the fourth!".

"Serves you right for trying to pinch a playing member's car, son!"

"'Course it's late - it's coming from Hong Kong!"

"These motorists must think we're stupid. That's the 28th Tesco bar code sticker we've copped today!"

"My God! It's the ghosts of New Brighton Fairground!"

"Some of the die-hard commuters never accepted the line closing......"

"I see the Baxter Museum is on the move again......"

"Why do they call them "Travelling People" when they never have any petrol?"

LIVERPOOL FERRY VIDEO
AND ON YOUR LEFT YOU'LL SEE.....
I REMEMBER WHEN IT COST FOURPENCE AND WE DIDN'T 'AVE TO LISTEN TO THIS RUBBISH!

*"Susan dear, remember - this is Wirral **LADIES!**"*

"Ring for an ambulance - the old boy's had a funny turn - it's the first time in his life all four bridges were working in the same week!"

"I'd've liked gnomes & a waterfall, but he got it in a sale at Cammel Laird!"

THE BLACK HORSE
HESWALL
I AM THE GHOST OF HESWALL CASTLE!
(NEVER 'EARD OF IT— CLEAR OFF!

"Move 'er along son - believe me - she's not from Birkenhead Priory!"

"She refuses to take them off - ever since she found out that she occupies the room Ian Botham was born in!"

"Don't put that up - well be overrun with Travelling People!"

"It's free, it's green & it's selling like hot cakes!"

"_AND_ it's starting to rain!"

"Go on give us a kiss - __IMAGINE__ we're under the Pier!"

"The've had quite a few wallies on there, over the years......"

"Yeah, I thumped him. Some University type doin' a survey. He said Wirral was a Peninsula!"

HAS THE TIDE BEEN IN THIS MONTH?
YES IT HAS. THE MOPED'S MOVED.
WELCOME TO PARKGATE

"Soon, a tall dark stranger will steal your milk......"

*"We could really screw things up with **<u>TRIPLE</u>** roundabouts!"*

"Go on motorists - make my day!"

"I wonder if he'll bring his bike?"

"He doesn't mind coming to the new Upton Sainsbury's, but he's not much help!"

Eventually, it will be recycled through the community - the seats will probably go next!"

"They're letting old stock go dead cheap!"

"'Course, he made all his money from heart surgery......."

"You want to put in for that Kevin...."

"We have to go straight on - this is a Ford!"

The West Kirby topless bathing ban officially applies to females Major, but we have had a couple of complaints about you, too......"

WEST KIRBY SENSIBILITIES · · · · ·

"There goes the Chris Boardman of Balls Road......"

"We have quite an elderly population in West Kirby......"

"Forget it love, the baths are shut!"

"I have this dream: I go into Sainsbury's Prenton, ask for an Asda produ[ct],
put it in a Kwiksave bag & wake up in Tesco Bidston!"

"Hey - Guess what? I know where I can lay my hands
on 98 miles of railing - dead cheap!"

"I wonder if they'll ever run a short ships' race?"